KiDs I.Q. PuZZLeS

LAGOON
BOOKS

Series Editor: Colleen Collier
Puzzle Writers: Anna Claybourne, Lloyd King
Maze Compiler: Adrian Fisher
Contributor: Sue Curran
Page Design & Layout: Gary Inwood Studios
Cover & Character Illustrations: Gary Sherwood
Puzzle Illustrations: Anni Jenkins

Published by:
LAGOON BOOKS
PO BOX 311, KT2 5QW, UK
PO BOX 990676, Boston, MA 02199, USA

www.lagoongames.com

ISBN: 1–902813–46–4

Printed in Singapore

Hey Kids! – meet Mac the Mathemagician

He has put together this exciting book especially with you in mind, and wants you to enjoy lots of fun mazes and puzzles that will help to make you even brainier than you already are!

Every puzzle has a star rating underneath the title, so that you can see how difficult it is before you try to answer it. And at the bottom of each page, you will find which page the answer to the puzzle is on. If you get it right, you can add the star points to your total. At the very end of the book, Mac has written out the maximum total of points you could get if you answer them all correctly. How many points can you get? Will you be able to get them all right? Mac thinks you can.

The other great thing about this book is that these types of puzzles will also help you develop your brain. The more of them you do, the easier they will become. And they're great fun too!

Have fun – and remember to see how many times you can spot Mac throughout the book!

Lunch Date

Lady Lucy Logic loves puzzles, so she tests her friends by wearing different colors of hats to lunch each day. What color should she wear on Friday?

Monday   Tuesday   Wednesday   Thursday

ANSWER ON PAGE 61

CHRistMas CracKer

★

Which one of these Christmas trees is the odd one out?

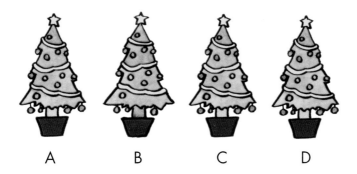

A   B   C   D

ANSWER ON PAGE 61

Butterfly Beauty

★

What number do you get if you divide the total number of butterflies by the total number of flowers?

ANSWER ON PAGE 62

TiLE CRazy

★ ★

This is the pattern of tiles on the floor of St Confused's Church. Going by the rest of the pattern, can you tell how many green tiles there are hidden under the rug?

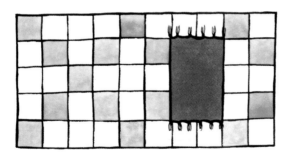

ANSWER ON PAGE 62

Laura's Lollipops

★

Laura has eaten three lollipops, but she wants another. What she doesn't realize is that Mrs Mindboggle, the shopkeeper, has been pulling them out of the jar in a special order. Which lollipop will she pull out next?

ANSWER ON PAGE 63

CREATURE COMFORTS

⭐

Which one of these animals is the odd one out?

ANSWER ON PAGE 63

Hop, Skip and Jump
★ ★

Help the frog jump across the lily pond. She can make short hops (one space) and long hops (two spaces) alternately, and can start with either one or two. But she cannot move diagonally.

 Start 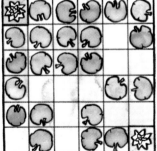 Finish

ANSWER ON PAGE 64

Counting Candles

★

Amy's sister has turned 12 today, and she has made a birthday cake for her. How many candles has she forgotten to put on?

ANSWER ON PAGE 64

Letter Dilemma

★

Which three letters will complete the sequence?

JFMAMJJAS

ANSWER ON PAGE 65

9

RiNG RiNG

Your granny is trying to call to wish you a Happy Birthday. Which phone line will allow you to speak to her?

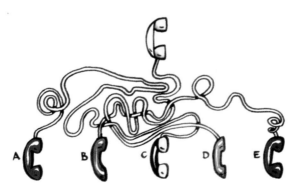

ANSWER ON PAGE 65

Tick Tock

★ ★

What time will this clock show in two hours and fifteen minutes when the alarm will go off?

ANSWER ON PAGE 66

Shapes and Stars

★

Which shape below is the next one in the series?

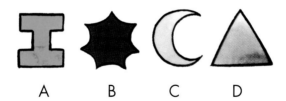

A   B   C   D

ANSWER ON PAGE 66

Animal Antics

★

Fill in the red squares in this grid so that there is a different type of animal in each row. When you've finished, the red squares can then be rearranged to name a type of plant. What is it?

ANSWER ON PAGE 67

Square Maze

★

Start at the bottom entrance, and find your way to the square in the middle of the maze.

ANSWER ON PAGE 67

14

Smokey the Clown
★

Can you find three differences between these two pictures of Smokey the Clown?

ANSWER ON PAGE 68

FISHY FRIENDS

⭐

How many fish and how many turtles can you spot?

ANSWER ON PAGE 68

Sign Language

★ ★

Theseus is stuck in a labyrinth, but fortunately he knows how to get out. All he has to do is follow a sequence of signs. Can you tell which sign Theseus should be looking for next?

A B C

ANSWER ON PAGE 69

BLackouT!

⭐

Which of the three buildings below has the correct number of lights needed to complete the series?

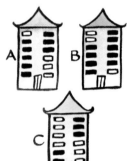

ANSWER ON PAGE 69

18

Lots of Spots

★

Which one of the following three dice comes next in the series?

 A   B   C

ANSWER ON PAGE 70

What's Next?

★

What should the next number in this sequence be?

ANSWER ON PAGE 70

Reach for the Moon
★ ★

Start at either of the two doors and find the path to the moon. Make sure you choose a different color path each time you pass through a window.

ANSWER ON PAGE 71

Spooky Sums

★ ★

What number do you get if you multiply the number of pumpkins by the number of ghosts, and then subtract the number of witches?

ANSWER ON PAGE 71

Square Eyes

★

How many squares can you see in this grid?

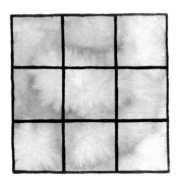

ANSWER ON PAGE 72

23

Flower Power

★

What is the missing number?

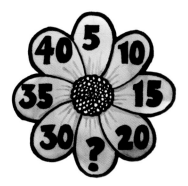

ANSWER ON PAGE 72

DiNNER PARty PLACES
★ ★

Bill Boffin is having guests to dinner and wants to make sure the place mats form a pattern around the table. Which place mat will go in Penny Polygon's place?

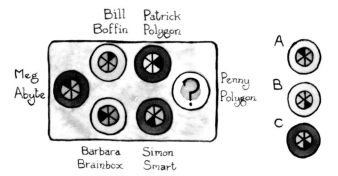

Bill Boffin   Patrick Polygon

Meg Abyte

Penny Polygon

Barbara Brainbox   Simon Smart

A

B

C

ANSWER ON PAGE 73

MatcH Magic

⭐

Move one match to leave 'nine'.

ANSWER ON PAGE 73

FRUIT BOX

Can you put these fruits in the crate so that no fruit is next to another one of the same type, in the same row (they **can** be next to each other diagonally).

ANSWER ON PAGE 74

Leaping Lizards
★ ★

Starting at the Blue Lizard, move from leaf to leaf until you reach the Green Lizard. But make sure you follow the paths in a Green-Blue-Red color sequence each time.

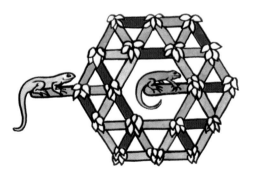

ANSWER ON PAGE 74

Odds and Evens
★ ★

Add all the even numbers together and what do you get?

ANSWER ON PAGE 75

Animal Magic

★

Wartbrain the Wizard is changing the shape of his assistant, Ellie. He changes her into...

What will he change her into next?

ANSWER ON PAGE 75

ANYONE FOR SUGAR?

★

Can you work out how many sugar lumps should come next?

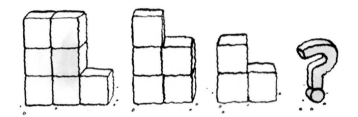

ANSWER ON PAGE 76

31

WHICH LETTER?

There's only one letter that can be used to fill in all the spaces in this grid, to make every row of letters into a word. What is it?

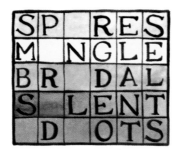

ANSWER ON PAGE 76

Candy Crisis

★ ★

Paula, Claire, Tom and Joe eat a total of 22 pieces of candy. If Paula eats seven pieces, Claire eats three, and Tom eats two, how many pieces of candy does Joe eat?

ANSWER ON PAGE 77

BABY BLOCKS

★ ★

Baby Bert is playing with his letter blocks and has made three words…

Only one of the following words will continue the sequence. Which one is it?

A DUCK   B DOG

C DADDY   D EGGS

ANSWER ON PAGE 77

34

MAZE MAYHEM
★ ★ ★

Start at the yellow path at the bottom and find your way to the purple square in the middle, by choosing a different color path each time you pass through a square.

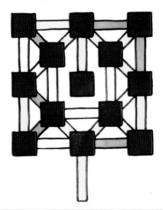

ANSWER ON PAGE 78

WHICH WAY?

⭐ ⭐

Can you fill in the next arrow in the series?

A  B C D

ANSWER ON PAGE 78

36

Side Show

★ ★

How many sides in total do three dice have?

ANSWER ON PAGE 79

Paper Chain Puzzle

★

Paul is making a paper chain to decorate his house at Christmas. He's only got red and green paper loops, so he's arranging them in a nice pattern. What color does he need next?

ANSWER ON PAGE 79

MaN's BEst FRieNd
★

Add the last match to leave a type of animal.

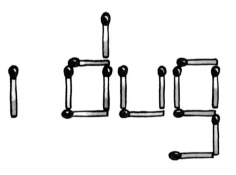

ANSWER ON PAGE 80

39

Going Bananas!
★ ★

Josh buys a banana and a coconut for $1.57 at the store. If the coconut costs 61 cents, how much does the banana cost?

ANSWER ON PAGE 80

APPLE MAGIC

★ ★ ★

Anna needs to take ten apples out of this crate to make an apple pie, but she wants to leave at least two apples in each row and two in each column as well. Can you help her?

ANSWER ON PAGE 81

41

Traffic Trauma

⭐ ⭐

Starting at the bottom, follow a Red-Amber-Green sequence of colors to reach the 'F' in the middle.

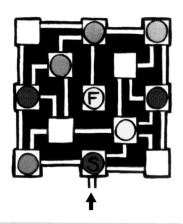

ANSWER ON PAGE 81

Dino Dilemma

★ ★

Alice bought a new pet Stegosaurus on Saturday, but unfortunately it gets bigger and eats more and more food every day! How many buns will she need to feed it on Wednesday?

Saturday	1 bun
Sunday	3 buns
Monday	7 buns
Tuesday	15 buns!
Wednesday	?

ANSWER ON PAGE 82

Shapes and Sides

★ ★

What is the missing number?

ANSWER ON PAGE 82

HIDDEN NUMBER

★

Can you add one match to leave a number?

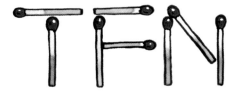

ANSWER ON PAGE 83

Shape Shifter

★ ★

What will be the next two shapes after these three?

ANSWER ON PAGE 83

ACES HIGH
⭐ ⭐

Which card has a mistake?

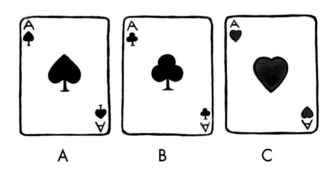

A   B   C

ANSWER ON PAGE 84

ADD UP

★ ★ ★

What is the missing number?

ANSWER ON PAGE 84

X Marks the Spot
★ ★ ★

Find your way to the X in the middle by changing path color every time you pass through a square.

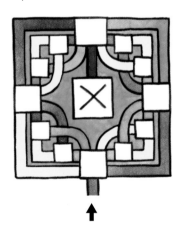

ANSWER ON PAGE 85

16

Put these numbers in the square so that each side always adds up to 16.

1 2 3 3 4 4 5 5 6 6 7 8

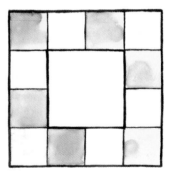

ANSWER ON PAGE 85

WORLD TOUR

★

The Browns are on a tour around the world. They've already been to Alaska, Ethiopia, and then Iceland. Where do you think they'll go next?

ANSWER ON PAGE 86

Going Dotty

⭐ ⭐

Fill in the missing spots on the second to last dice to complete the series.

ANSWER ON PAGE 86

Dots and Spots

★ ★ ★

Can you work out which of the tiles below would complete the pattern in this grid?

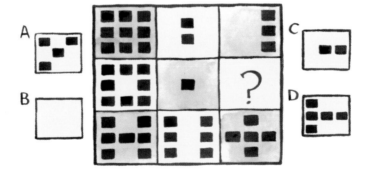

ANSWER ON PAGE 87

Circles and Stars
⭐ ⭐ ⭐

If ⭐ = 3 points and ⬤ = 4 points, how many points does 🔲 equal?

ANSWER ON PAGE 87

PLANE PROBLEM

★

Captain Rosa Seats can't fly her plane until someone fills in the missing numbers on this dial. Can you help?

ANSWER ON PAGE 88

Hexagon Heaven
★ ★ ★

Start at the bottom and follow the paths to reach the circle in the middle.

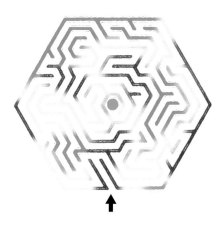

ANSWER ON PAGE 88

MUSHROOM MAGIC

How many toadstools should appear next?

     ?

ANSWER ON PAGE 89

57

FrUity FUn

Mr Fruitbasket is stocking his store shelves with fruit and vegetables.

What comes next in the sequence? Should it be Apples, Lemons, Melons or Celery?

ANSWER ON PAGE 89

NAUGHTY NUMBERS

⭐ ⭐ ⭐

Can you work out what number is missing from this grid?

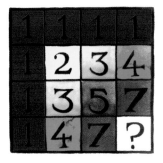

ANSWER ON PAGE 90

MILES OF TILES

★ ★ ★

Professor G. O'Metric is tiling his bathroom with a sequence of different tiles. Can you work out which one will be next?

    ?

A   B   C  D

ANSWER ON PAGE 90

Solutions

Scores

Page 1 – **Lunch Date** ★

She should wear blue on Friday because she is working through the colors of the rainbow (red, orange, yellow, green, blue, indigo, and violet).

Friday

Page 2 – **Christmas Cracker** ★

The answer is B, because the bauble at the bottom right corner of this tree is missing.

B

Solutions

Scores

Page 3 – BUTTERFLY BEAUTY

8 $\div\ 4$ $=\ 2$

Page 4 – TILE CRAZY ★ ★

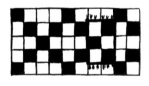

There are three green tiles
hidden under the rug.

Solutions

Scores

Page 5 – Laura's Lollipops

A – each time, the number of spots on the lollipops goes up one.

Page 6 – Creature Comforts

The rabbit – it is facing the opposite direction to the others.

Solutions

....

Page 7 – Hop, Skip and Jump

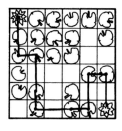

This is just one way of doing it – can you find another?

....

Page 8 – Counting Candles

$12 - 8 = 4$

Solutions

Scores

Page 9 – **Letter Dilemma** ⭐

They stand for October, November, and December, because the letters are the initials of the months of the year.

Page 10 – **Ring Ring** ⭐ ⭐

Solutions

Scores

....

Page 11 – Tick Tock

★ ★

The answer is five o'clock exactly.

....

Page 12 – Shapes and Stars

★

D – the triangle, because with each step, the number of points on the shape goes down by one.

D

Solutions

Scores

Page 13 – **Animal Antics** ★

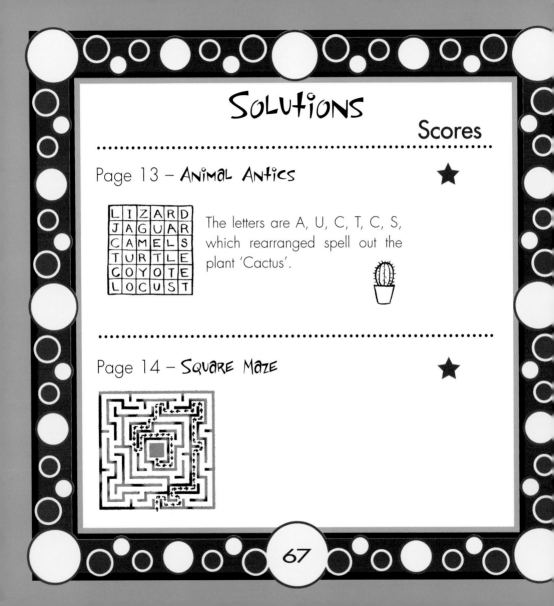

L	I	Z	A	R	D
J	A	G	U	A	R
C	A	M	E	L	S
T	U	R	T	L	E
C	O	Y	O	T	E
L	O	C	U	S	T

The letters are A, U, C, T, C, S, which rearranged spell out the plant 'Cactus'.

Page 14 – **Square Maze** ★

67

Solutions

Scores

....

Page 15 – SMOKEY THE CLOWN ★

....

Page 16 – FISHY FRIENDS ★

 = 9

 = 5

Solutions

....

Page 17 – Sign Language

A – the number of spots around the edge of the signs goes up by one each time.

A

....

Page 18 – Blackout!

The answer is B.

B

Solutions

....

Page 19 – Lots of Spots

The number of spots goes up by one each time, so the answer is B.

B

....

Page 20 – What's Next?

16

The number increases by one, then two, then three, then four and then five, so the answer is 16.

Solutions

Scores

Page 21 – Reach for the Moon

Page 22 – Spooky Sums

$$3 \,🎃 \times 3 \,👻 = 9$$

$$9 - 4 \,🧙 = 5$$

Solutions

Scores

....

Page 23 – SQUARE EYES

There are 14 squares hidden, including single squares, squares made up of four single squares, and the outside square.

....

Page 24 – FLOWER POWER

25

Solutions

Scores

Page 25 – DiNNeR PaRty PLaCeS

 GREEN B – the black box moves around each of the six sections and the background color alternates between purple and green, so the correct one has to be green.

B

Page 26 – MatcH MaGic

73

Solutions

Scores

Page 27 – **Fruit Box**

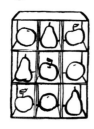

This is one possible solution, but there are others.

Page 28 – **Leaping Lizards**

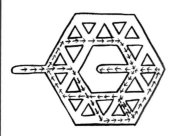

Solutions

Page 29 – Odds and Evens ★ ★

$$2+4+8=14$$

Page 30 – Animal Magic ★

A spider – the number of legs increases by two each time.

Solutions

Page 31 – ANYONE FOR SUGAR?

Each stack of sugar cubes contains two less than the previous one, so the answer is one.

Page 32 – WHICH LETTER?

Spires
Mingle
Bridal
Silent
Idiots

76

Solutions

Scores

Page 33 – Candy Crisis

$$22 - 7 - 3 - 2 = 10$$

Page 34 – Baby Blocks

B

Both the first letter and the last letter of each word move forwards through the alphabet, so the answer has to be 'Dog', which is B.

77

Solutions

....

Page 35 – MAZE MAYHEM   ★ ★ ★

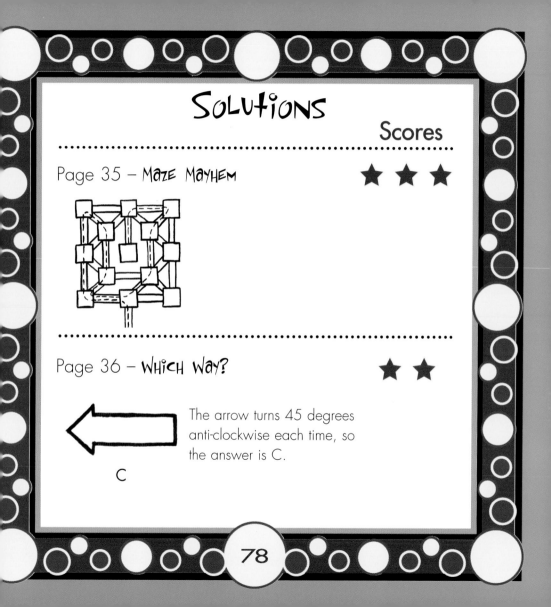

....

Page 36 – WHICH WAY?   ★ ★

The arrow turns 45 degrees anti-clockwise each time, so the answer is C.

C

Solutions

Scores

Page 37 – **Side Show**

Each dice has six sides, so the answer is 3 dice x 6 sides which equals 18.

Page 38 – **Paper Chain Puzzle**

GREEN

There is a pattern of one of the first color, followed by two of the other color, alternately repeated along the chain. So the answer is Green.

Solutions

....

Page 39 – Man's Best Friend

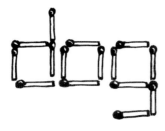

....

Page 40 – Going Bananas!

$1.57 – 61 = 96 cents

Solutions

Scores

....

Page 41 – **APPLE Magic**

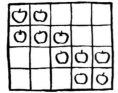

....

Page 42 – **Traffic Trauma**

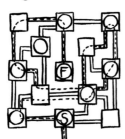

Solutions

Scores

Page 43 – Dino Dilemma

★ ★

31 buns

Each day, Alice has to double the number of buns from the previous day and then add one, so the number of buns for Wednesday has to be 31.

Page 44 – Shapes and Sides

★ ★

5

The number inside each shape is the same as the number of sides the shape has, so the answer is 5.

Solutions

Scores

Page 45 – HIDDEN NUMBER ★

Page 46 – SHAPE SHIFTER ★ ★

Each shape is a letter of the alphabet turned on its side and flipped over to show its mirror image. So the next two letters will be D and E.

Solutions

Page 47 – ACES HIGH

The answer is B, because the club in the bottom right corner should be the other way round.

B

Page 48 – ADD UP

The numbers in each circle add up to 20, so the answer is 8.

84

Solutions

Scores

Page 49 – X Marks the Spot

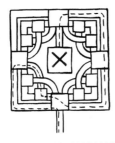

Page 50 – **16**

1	6	7	2
4			5
8			5
3	3	6	4

85

SOLUTIONS

Scores

Page 51 – WORLD TOUR

Each of their destinations begin with a different vowel, moving forwards through the alphabet, so the next place they'll visit has to be Oman.

Page 52 – GOING DOTTY

86

Solutions

....

Page 53 – Dots and Spots

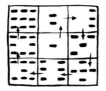

The answer is Tile A, which has four spots on it. The tiles spiral out from the center, adding an extra spot each time.

....

Page 54 – Circles and Stars

$\square = 6$

$9 + 16 = 25$
$25 - 24 = 1$
$24 \div 4 = 6$

87

Solutions

Scores

Page 55 – PLANE PROBLEM ⭐

The number doubles each time around the circle – 1 x 2 = 2, 2 x 2 = 4, 4 x 2 = 8, 8 x 2 = 16, 16 x 2 = 32. The answer is therefore 16.

Page 56 – HEXAGON HEAVEN ⭐ ⭐ ⭐

Solutions

....

Page 57 – MUSHROOM MAGIC

The answer is 5.

....

Page 58 – FRUITY FUN

The initial letters of each fruit or vegetable move backwards through the alphabet, so the last one must be 'L' for 'Lemons'.

Solutions

Scores

....

Page 59 – Naughty Numbers

The first row and column increase by zero each time, the second row and column by one each time, the third row and column by two each time, and so the missing number is ten (increased by three).

....

Page 60 – Miles of Tiles

The answer is B.

B

....

MAXIMUM TOTAL = 104

LAGOON WEB SITE

Games, Books, Puzzles and Gizmos

Visit the Lagoon Web Site to view a
staggering range of fantastic games,
puzzles and books to suit all.

www.lagoongames.com

Adrian Fisher Maze Design
www.mazemaker.com

OTHER TITLES BY LAGOON BOOKS

Kids Maze Puzzle Books

Wanda the Witch and the Magical Maze
(1-902813-11-1)

Dr CK Fortune and the Lost City Labyrinth
(1-902813-12-X)

Internet Web Site Book

500 of the Coolest Sites for Cyberkids
(1-902813-27-8)

LAGOON
BOOKS